Kay & Ray
Bible Stories for Today's Children

Listening to Mom

#3 - JONAH AND THE WHALE

Written by
Debbie Henderson Maestas

Illustrated by
Andrew Thomas

ISBN Hardback: 978-1-7326571-6-8
ISBN Paperback: 978-1-7326571-7-5

Library of Congress Control Number: 2019913206

Printed in the United States of America, September 2019

Be Still Publications
Houston, Texas

Be Still
Publications

Author photo by Tiffany Maestas

Dedication

This book, and all books in the series, are dedicated to the memories of both my brother, Dave, and father, Ray. Their faith in God and their courage fighting cancer have inspired me to follow my dreams.

It is my prayer that all children (and adults) reading my books will be delighted with the stories, be encouraged to read their Bibles, and will continue to develop their faith and relationship with God, Jesus, and the Holy Spirit.

Reviews

"Reading the third book in Debbie's Kay and Ray series is like spending time in the warmth of the author's own presence. Not only do the characters as drawn resemble Debbie and her beloved brother, but the tone of the work reflects much of her own character and disposition. Debbie's tale, rooted as it is in the Biblical tale of Jonah, entirely avoids offering a sermon, or preaching to its young audience. The central conflict occurs when Kay, a typical child, chooses to ignore her mother's instructions in delaying her inevitable chores. In response, both big brother Ray and their mother avoid scoldings, instead encouraging right action by example, Ray with his industry and generosity, Mom in her nurturing forgiveness. Young readers will identify with the authentic characters, and will discover the story's lesson without realizing they have been instructed. Thankfully, there are many more Bible stories to draw from, and we can look forward to more voyages into the world of Kay and Ray."

--Marta Crawford, High School English Teacher and mother of two

Reviews

"The book, Listening to Mom is a good example of God's love and forgiveness to us all. The author Debbie Henderson Maestas does a wonderful job showing this. When Kay was asked to do her daily chores, she finds every excuse not to do them. Her consequence is losing out on some of her favorite rewards. Her brother Ray shows God's compassion by lending a helping hand to do these chores. This book is a perfect example of God's love, and why we should obey our parents. Hopefully Kay learned from this experience."

--Glenda Mouton, Early Childhood Educator in Christian/Public Schools 40+ years.

"If you've ever been a kid or the parent of one, this story about Kay is a familiar scene. Debbie does a great job of taking an everyday rebellion like not doing your chores and connecting the story of Jonah. Truth is, I need this reminder as a grown up too."

-- Paul Foster, dad with four boys

Free Coloring Book

Join my mailing list and receive a free coloring book:

https://www.subscribepage.com/coloringbook

Your information will remain confidential and be used only for notifying you of my upcoming books, promotions, events, or occasional newsletters. You may unsubscribe anytime.

Books by Debbie

Helping a Neighbor

#1 - The Good Samaritan

--Hardback: 978-1-7326571-0-6
--Paperback: 978-1-7326571-1-3

Finding a Freind

#2 - The Lost Sheep

--Hardback: 978-1-7326571-3-7
--Paperback: 978-1-7326571-4-4

My big brother, Ray, is always a great helper, even when I don't want to listen to Mom and Dad.

I remember the week I didn't listen to Mom when she asked me to do chores.

That was a big mistake!

Mom had given Ray and me each a small list of chores to do. Of course, Ray did his right away.

I didn't feel like doing my list. I wanted to go play instead. It's much more fun to play than work.

My best friend, Tommy, got a new game for his birthday, and I wanted to go play it with him.

After school, I snuck out of the house and went to see Tommy. We had lots of fun playing together.

When I got back home, I thought no one knew I had left the house.

But I was wrong.

The pizza delivery guy was dropping off my favorite pizza. I was excited about the yummy dinner.

When we sat down to dinner Mom gave me a bologna sandwich and a side dish of peas instead of the pizza.

I hate peas!!

17

Mom asked if there was anything I'd like to tell her about my day. Dad and Ray looked at me with disappointment in their eyes.

I gulped.

I told them I went to Tommy's instead of doing my chores. Mom said that's why they all got pizza and I didn't.

19

The next day Mom reminded me to do my chores.

I still didn't feel like doing them. I was mad about the pizza dinner I didn't get to enjoy.

Instead of doing my chores I went out back to play in my tree house that Dad and Ray had built for me.

23

24

I was having a terrific time in the tree house with my dolls and tea party set.

25

The sound of the ice cream truck coming down our street made me stop playing. Mom sometimes gave Ray and me money to buy ice cream treats.

I hoped today she would let us have some. I decided to come down from the tree house.

The folding ladder for the tree house was next to the door. I went to extend it so I could climb down, and it broke off the hinge.

Now how was I going to get down? I couldn't call out to my family because then they would know I was in the tree house instead of doing my chores.

I heard the ice cream truck leaving our neighborhood. Tears came to my eyes when I saw Ray come into the backyard licking an ice cream cone!

Mom had given him money for the treat.

First, I missed out on pizza and then I didn't get any ice cream.

CHORES

Kay	Ray
☐ laundry	☑ vacuum
☐ clean room	☑ dusting
☐ mop	☑ water plants
☐ dishes	☑ sweep

I was beginning to think that maybe I should have done my chores right when Mom told me to do them.

Ray saw me in the tree house and brought over the extension ladder from the garage. He helped me down and asked if I was ready to do my chores yet. I said yes.

He offered to help me get them done. I thanked Ray for helping me.

36

Then I told Mom I was sorry I didn't
do my chores right away. She said she
forgave me and hoped I had learned to
listen to her the first time she asked me
to do something. I said I did.

When we did our bedtime prayers, Ray read the Bible story about Jonah. He was a man who didn't want to listen to God, and he ended up inside a whale! Wow, what a story.

I'm glad I only missed out on pizza and ice cream. Thankfully Jonah and I learned to listen.

I'm glad Ray was there to help me. I know I can always count on my big brother, and I can always count on God.

Debbie Maestas has worked with children for over 25 years in various capacities and earned her Master of Arts in Teaching. She has taught kindergarten in public schools and prekindergarten in private Christian schools.

She loves traveling and has been to many places including Israel, Egypt, Greece, Australia, Tahiti, New Zealand, Canada, and Mexico.

Her happy place is the beach where she likes to walk near the ocean, listen to the waves, and talk with God. Debbie has a strong faith in God and wants to share His Word with children in a fun, age-appropriate style.

She is a member of SCBWI.

Get to know me and keep up with my writing by visiting my website and Facebook page.

https://www.debbiehmaestas.com

https://www.facebook.com/
AuthorDebbieHendersonMaestas

Andrew Thomas is an artist working in children's illustration and in animation. An illustrator of over fifteen published children's books, Andrew is passionate about the ability to inspire children through his work.

A devout Christian, Andrew loves helping bring the Kay and Ray series to life to spread God's message to the Christian youth.

Get to know Andrew by visiting his website:

https://www.andrewgthomas.com

Please leave a review

I would appreciate you leaving an honest review on the website where you purchased my book. It helps promote sales which in turn spreads God's word to children.

Thank you!!

Enjoy the first Kay & Ray book
in a Spanish edition:

Helping a Neighbor
Ayudando a un vecino

Coming out in December 2019.

CPSIA information can be obtained
at www.ICGtesting.com
Printed in the USA
LVHW061546230520
656346LV00012B/755

9 781732 657175